A Literature Kit™ FOR

Treasure Island

By Robert Louis Stevenson

Written by Brenda Rollins, Ed.D.

GRADES 7-8

Classroom Complete Press
P.O. Box 19729
San Diego, CA 92159
Tel: 1-800-663-3609 | Fax: 1-800-663-3608
Email: service@classroomcompletepress.com

www.classroomcompletepress.com

ISBN-13: 978-1-55319-385-2
ISBN-10: 1-55319-385-7
 We acknowledge the financial support of the Government of Canada through the Book Publishing Industry Development Program (BPIDP) for our publishing activities. Printed in Canada.

Critical Thinking Skills

Treasure Island

Level	Skills For Critical Thinking	1-4	5-8	9-12	13-15	16-18	19-21	22-24	25-27	28-31	32-34	Writing Tasks	Graphic Organizers
		Chapter Questions											
LEVEL 1 Remembering	• Identify Story Elements	✓			✓	✓	✓	✓			✓	✓	✓
	• Recall Details	✓	✓	✓	✓	✓	✓	✓	✓	✓	✓	✓	✓
	• Match	✓	✓	✓		✓	✓	✓	✓	✓	✓		
	• Sequence		✓				✓			✓	✓		
	• List	✓		✓	✓		✓	✓		✓	✓		✓
LEVEL 2 Understanding	• Compare Characters			✓		✓	✓		✓				✓
	• Summarize	✓	✓	✓	✓			✓	✓	✓	✓		
	• State Main Idea	✓			✓	✓		✓	✓	✓			✓
	• Describe	✓	✓	✓	✓	✓	✓	✓	✓	✓	✓		
	• Interpret		✓		✓	✓			✓			✓	✓
LEVEL 3 Applying	• Choose Information	✓		✓	✓	✓	✓	✓	✓	✓	✓		
	• Identify Outcomes		✓		✓				✓	✓			
	• Apply What is Learned	✓	✓	✓		✓	✓	✓		✓	✓		
	• Make Connections	✓	✓			✓	✓	✓	✓	✓	✓	✓	✓
LEVEL 4 Analysing	• Draw Conclusions	✓	✓		✓	✓	✓		✓		✓	✓	✓
	• Identify Supporting Evidence	✓		✓				✓	✓	✓		✓	
	• Infer Character Motivations		✓	✓	✓		✓	✓		✓			
	• Identify Cause & Effect	✓			✓		✓		✓		✓	✓	
	• Identify Relationships	✓	✓			✓		✓	✓	✓	✓		✓
LEVEL 5 Evaluating	• State & Defend an Opinion	✓		✓			✓			✓		✓	
	• Make Judgments	✓	✓	✓	✓	✓	✓	✓		✓	✓		
	• Explain		✓	✓	✓		✓		✓	✓	✓	✓	
LEVEL 6 Creating	• Predict		✓		✓		✓				✓	✓	
	• Design	✓	✓	✓		✓			✓			✓	
	• Create	✓	✓			✓	✓		✓		✓	✓	
	• Imagine Alternatives			✓		✓			✓			✓	

Based on Bloom's Taxonomy

Contents

Assessment Rubric

Treasure Island

Student's Name: ______________________ Assignment: ________________ Level: ________

	Level 1	Level 2	Level 3	Level 4
Comprehension of the Novel	• Demonstrates a limited understanding of the novel. Requires teacher intervention.	• Demonstrates a basic understanding of the novel's content.	• Demonstrates a good understanding of the novel's content.	• Demonstrates a thorough understanding of the novel's content.
Response to the Text	• Expresses responses to the text with limited effectiveness, inconsistently supported by proof from the text.	• Expresses responses to the text with some effectiveness, supported with some proof from the text.	• Expresses responses to the text with appropriate skills, supported with appropriate proof from the text.	• Expresses thorough and complete responses to the text, supported by concise and effective proof from the text.
Interpretation and Analysis	• Interprets and explains various elements of the text with few, unrelated details and incorrect analysis.	• Interprets and explains various elements of the text with some detail, but with some inconsistent analysis.	• Interprets and explains various elements of the text with appropriate detail and analysis.	• Effectively interprets and explains various elements of the text with consistent, clear and effective detail and analysis

STRENGTHS:

WEAKNESSES:

NEEDS IMPROVEMENT:

Teacher Guide

Our resource has been created for ease of use by both TEACHERS and STUDENTS alike.

Introduction

__Treasure Island__ was first published in 1883, although it had appeared initially in Young Folks in serial form July 1881-June 1882 under the alternative title of "The Sea-Cook or Treasure Island". The book was developed from an imaginary map that Stevenson and his stepson, Lloyd Osbourne, had made while on vacation. Perhaps, this is the reason for the book's allure to children. Also, the famous pirate, Long John Silver, was the invention of Stevenson's friend, William Henley. __Treasure Island__ is one of the most perfect examples of an exciting adventure tale of all time.

How Is Our Literature Kit™ Organized?

STUDENT HANDOUTS

Chapter Activities *(in the form of reproducible worksheets)* make up the majority of our resource. For each chapter there are BEFORE YOU READ activities and AFTER YOU READ activities.

- The BEFORE YOU READ activities prepare students for reading by setting a purpose for reading. They stimulate background knowledge and experience, and guide students to make connections between what they know and what they will learn. Important concepts and vocabulary from the chapter(s) are also presented.
- The AFTER YOU READ activities check students' comprehension and extend their learning. Students are asked to give thoughtful consideration of the text through creative and evaluative short-answer questions and journal prompts. Word Study activities are also included for some of the chapters.

Six **Writing Tasks** and three **Graphic Organizers** are included to further develop students' critical thinking and writing skills, and analysis of the text. *(See page 6 for suggestions on using the Graphic Organizers.)* The **Assessment Rubric** *(page 4)* is a useful tool for evaluating students' responses to the Writing Tasks and Graphic Organizers.

PICTURE CUES

Our resource contains three main types of pages, each with a different purpose and use. A **Picture Cue** at the top of each page shows, at a glance, what the page is for.

Teacher Guide
- Information and tools for the teacher

Student Handout
- Reproducible worksheets and activities

Easy Marking™ Answer Key
- Answers for student activities

EASY MARKING™ ANSWER KEY

Marking students' worksheets is fast and easy with our **Answer Key**. Answers are listed in columns – just line up the column with its corresponding worksheet, as shown, and see how every question matches up with its answer!

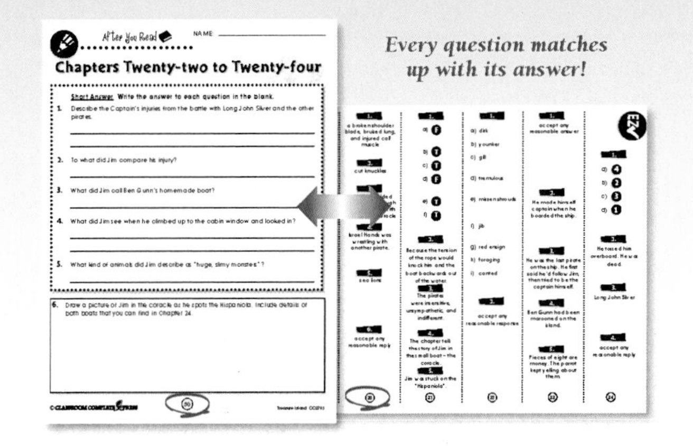

1,2,3

Graphic Organizers

The three **Graphic Organizers** included in our Literature Kit™ are especially suited to a study of ***Treasure Island***. Below are suggestions for using each organizer in your classroom, or they may be adapted to suit the individual needs of your students. The organizers can be used on a projection system or interactive whiteboard in teacher-led activities, and/or photocopied for use as student worksheets. To evaluate students' responses to any of the organizers, you may wish to use the **Assessment Rubric** *(on page 4)*.

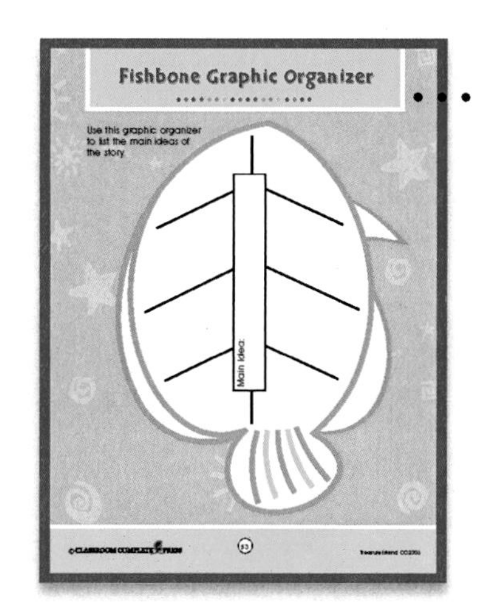

FISH BONE ORGANIZER CHART

This graphic organizer is a particularly effective tool to aid students in identifying the main ideas and supporting details of the story. The Fish Bone organizer chart may be used to enable the students to isolate the main idea and supporting details of each chapter or section. After the book is finished, these charts are excellent tools for students to use when they summarize the book.

Found on Page 53.

SENSORY DETAIL CHART

This graphic organizer helps students look for descriptive details that appeal to one or more of their five senses as they read. Good readers use all their senses to help them fully grasp what they are reading. They use their imagination to help them see what the author is writing and to hear what the language sounds like. This method asks readers to pay specific attention to the sensory details of what they read to help them better understand what the text is saying. *Treasure Island* is a goldmine of sensory details waiting to be explored.

Found on Page 54.

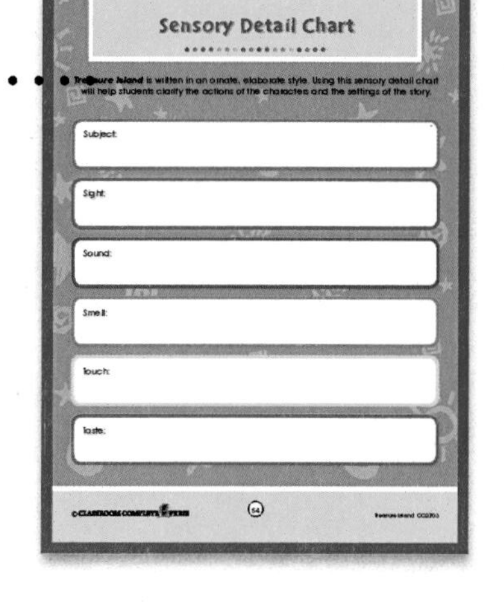

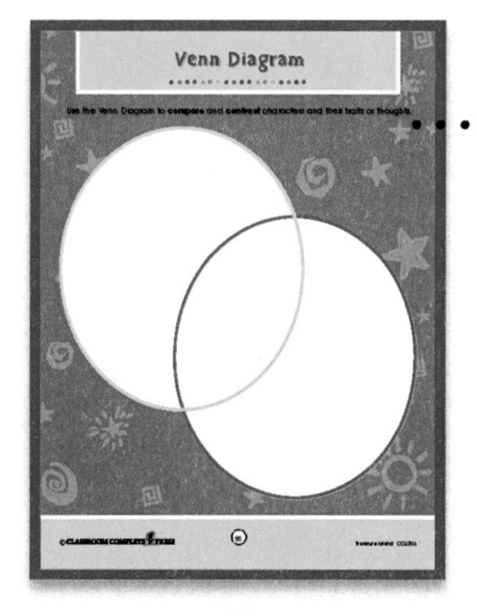

VENN DIAGRAM

This graphic organizer asks readers to compare and contrast different ideas, texts, authors, characters, eras - and to identify the ways in which they are similar and different. Students may wish to use a Venn diagram to compare two similar characters such as Jim and Captain Smollett, or to contrast two dissimilar characters such as the Doctor and Long John Silver.

Found on Page 55.

Bloom's Taxonomy* for Reading Comprehension

The activities in this resource engage and build the full range of thinking skills that are essential for students' reading comprehension. Based on the six levels of thinking in Bloom's Taxonomy, questions are given that challenge students to not only recall what they have read, but move beyond this to understand the text through higher-order thinking. By using higher-order skills of applying, analysing, evaluating and creating, students become active readers, drawing more meaning from the text, and applying and extending their learning in more sophisticated ways.

This **Literature Kit**™, therefore, is an effective tool for any Language Arts program. Whether it is used in whole or in part, or adapted to meet individual student needs, this resource provides teachers with the important questions to ask, inspiring students' interest, creativity, and promoting meaningful learning.

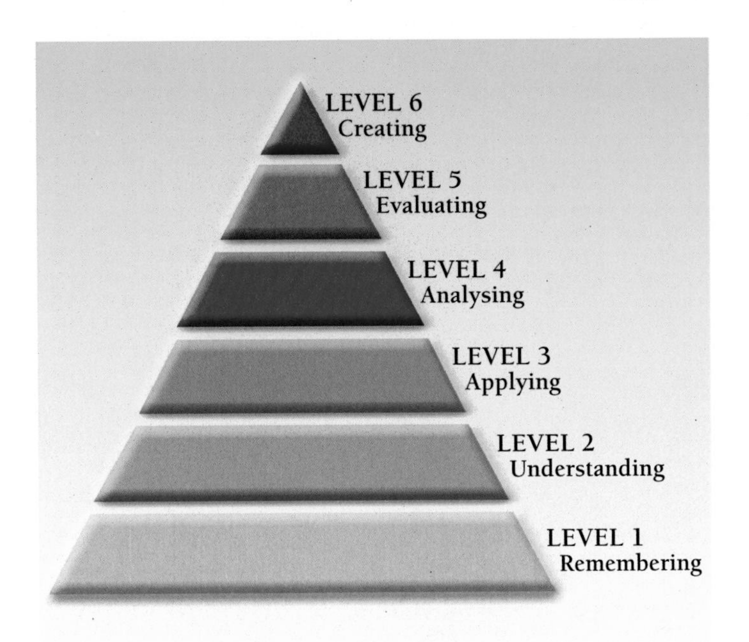

BLOOM'S TAXONOMY: 6 LEVELS OF THINKING

***Bloom's Taxonomy is a widely used tool by educators for classifying learning objectives, and is based on the work of Benjamin Bloom.**

Teaching Strategies

WHOLE-CLASS, SMALL GROUP AND INDEPENDENT STUDY

There are several ways to teach the novel, **Treasure Island**. You may wish to use the classic "whole class read-aloud" method along with some shared or modeled reading, focusing on the author's skills and the elements of the narrative. Both the *"Before You Read"* and *"After You Read"* activities in this Literature Kit provide many opportunities for discussion. The division of content into chapter groupings should facilitate independent study which will allow students to work on easily read sections of the novel at a time.

Another teaching method is to use the book as a source of small group activities which focus on various aspects of the story and characterizations. Loyalty, deceit, greed, and violence are major themes which may be studied and discussed. One way to study these qualities is to divide the class into several small groups and have each group investigate the relationships between various characters such as Jim and Long John Silver or Jim and the Doctor. Other activities which add to the novel's meaning include character descriptions, character portraits, and alternative endings. Students often enjoy writing a "what happened next?" story to continue the saga of Jim and his companions – what did they do after they found the treasure? Whatever you choose, you will find that Treasure Island is one of the best adventure novels of all time.

Summary of the Story

TREASURE ISLAND is an adventure story full of danger, pirates, double-crossing, and, best of all, treasure.

Jim Hawkins is a young boy who lives with his mother and father in Bristol, England. They keep an inn for travelers, and one such traveler is Billy Bones. Billy stays, befriending young Jim before he dies after being served with a 'black spot' – a pirate verdict of guilt. Before Billy's pursuers can ransack the inn, Jim and his mother open Billy's chest to find a logbook and a map.

Jim takes the map to Dr. Livesey and Squire Trelawney. They recognize it to be the treasure map of Captain Flint. They quickly assemble a crew to set sail to Treasure Island. One of the members of the crew is a one legged cook named Long John Silver. Jim overhears Silver and his fellow crewmates planning a mutiny. Jim tells the captain, Captain Smollett, of the planned insurgence. Captain Smollett plans to give the mutineers shore-time when they land in order to delay any hostility, but Jim sneaks aboard the pirate's boat for more adventure.

While on shore, Jim witnesses Long John Silver murdering a crewmate who does not want to join the mutiny. Fearing for his life, Jim runs further on the island only to find a half-crazed man named Ben Gunn. Ben once served with Captain Flint's crew but was marooned on the island.

Jim takes Ben to Captain Smollett at the small stockade the pirates have built. Silver tries to negotiate with Smollett, but Smollett is wary to speak with him. Instead, he does not give him an audience. The pirates, then, attack the stockade wounding Captain Smollett. Jim is eager to take action and sets off on the island to find Ben Gunn's hidden boat.

After finding Gunn's boat, Jim plans to float to the ship and cut it free so the pirates have no way of leaving the island. But when he is caught by Israel Hands, Jim, in a fight for his life, kills Israel and is wounded himself.

Jim returns to the stockade, now overrun by the pirates, and is taken hostage. Long John Silver keeps his crew from killing the young boy, but he seems to be having trouble with his own men. The other pirates serve Silver with a 'black spot' deposing him as their commander. Long John Silver proceeds to tell them about the treasure in a desperate attempt to keep control.

The pirates, with Jim in tow, search for the treasure only to find the site excavated and empty. Ben Gunn had found the treasure months earlier and now had it hidden in a different location. Just before the pirates turn on each other in rage, Dr. Livesey, Ben Gunn, and others fire on the pirate band scattering them throughout the island. Silver and Jim flee together, and, with the help of Ben and the others, they set off to find the treasure.

With the treasure safely aboard the ship, the remaining crew leaves the mutineers stranded on the island. Long John Silver is allowed to join the ship going home, but he sneaks off with a portion of the treasure. Jim is now plagued with nightmares of gold coins and the sea.

Suggestions for Further Reading

OTHER BOOKS BY ROBERT LOUIS STEVENSON

Kidnapped *© 1886.*
Strange Case of Dr. Jekyll and Mr. Hyde *© 1886.*

OTHER RECOMMENDED RESOURCES

Mark Twain, ***The Adventures of Tom Sawyer*** *© 1876.*
Daniel Defoe, ***Robinson Crusoe*** *© 1719*
John Matthews, ***Pirates*** *© 2007.*

Vocabulary

CHAPTER 1:	• tarry • grog • diabolical • rebuff • hawker • hamlet • tallowy • seafaring • fawning • sneering • mutilated
CHAPTER 2:	• indignation • tallowy • seafaring • fawning • sneering • mutilated
CHAPTER 3:	• pitch • cutlass • apoplexy
CHAPTER 4:	• lugger • quadrant • oilskin
CHAPTER 5:	• miscreant • formidable • lubbers • buccaneers
CHAPTER 6:	• cache • atrocious • miscreant • bloodthirstiest
CHAPTER 7:	• calumnies • odious • tarpaulins • heath • dale
CHAPTER 8:	• quid • relinquishing • entertainment • dexterity
CHAPTER 9:	• swivel • garrison • patiently • berthed
CHAPTER 10:	• coxswain • lanyard • duff • stave
CHAPTER 11:	• Parliament • abominable • farthings • navigate
CHAPTER 12:	• conical • prodigious • countenance • duplicity
CHAPTER 13:	• becalmed • scuppers • conned • pikes
CHAPTER 14:	• undulating • fen • aperture • languor • modulated
CHAPTER 15:	• nondescript • apparition • incongruous • gaskin
CHAPTER 16:	• gig • cognac • palisade • abominable • stockade • jolly-boat
CHAPTER 17:	• gallipot • contrived • bombardment • tarpaulin • clustering
CHAPTER 18:	• stockade • mutineers • hesitation • molestation
CHAPTER 19:	• observation • cannonade • demolishing • parmesan
CHAPTER 20:	• placidly • avast • treacherous • surmounting
CHAPTER 21:	• drub • girdle • hurly-burly • hanger • sallied
CHAPTER 22:	• plaster • girt • brace • crags • spit • rogue • coracle • repulse
CHAPTER 23:	• hawser • gully • ditty • wrought
CHAPTER 24:	• crags • formidable • reverberations • credible
CHAPTER 25:	• foraging • bowspirit • schooner • bulwark
CHAPTER 26:	• canted • coxswain • Hispaniola • port scuppers
CHAPTER 27:	• tremulous • consequence • quivering • port shrouds
CHAPTER 28:	• link • smote • glim • truculently • puncheon
CHAPTER 29:	• batten down your hatches • emissary • hornpipe • environed
CHAPTER 30:	• pestiferous slough • slip your cable
CHAPTER 31:	• fried junk • slow-growing creeper • baccy box
CHAPTER 32:	• plateau • skylarking • precipices • volubly • conspicuous • countenance • underwood • cache
CHAPTER 33:	• prodigious • imposter • dereliction • obsequious
CHAPTER 34:	• humane • palisade • formidable

Robert Louis Stevenson (1850 - 1894)

Robert Louis Stevenson was born in November 1850 in Edinburgh, Scotland. Both his mother and father were from well-respected families, and Stevenson was expected to follow in his father's footsteps by becoming an engineer.

Robert was a good student with a promising career, so his father enrolled him at the Edinburgh University to study engineering. Stevenson, however, soon rebelled against this idea and chose to study law instead. Although he passed the bar at the age of twenty-five, he never practiced law. He traveled with his college friends to various countries in Europe and it was in this manner that Stevenson was first published. For several years, Robert Louis Stevenson was known for his essays and travel writings.

While on one of his trips, he met Fanny Van de Grift Osbourne, a thirty-six year old divorcee. Although she was ten years older than he, Stevenson fell madly in love. Both Stevenson and Osbourne traveled back to California to finalize her divorce. They were married immediately.

Osbourne had two children of her own when she and Stevenson married. Robert got along well with both children, but it was while playing with his step-son, Lloyd, that he got the idea for *Treasure Island*. They had painted a watercolor map of an imaginary island. *Treasure Island* was Stevenson's first real success.

Ironically, Stevenson's health caused him to look for more tropical climates to live in - an island of his own. He and his family traveled to the South Seas eventually setting up residence in Samoa. There he died in 1894. He is buried on top of Mount Vaea, but his characters live on in the hearts of millions.

Did You Know?

- **Robert Louis Stevenson's name used to be spelled "Lewis?" He changed it to rebel against his father's wishes!**
- **Stevenson wrote the first fifteen chapters of *Treasure Island* in fifteen days?**
- **Stevenson's father owned a company that made deep-sea lighthouses.**
- ***Treasure Island* has been filmed over twenty times!**

NAME: ______________________

Chapters One to Four

1. Have you ever found something mysterious? What did you do? What if you were to find a mysterious map? Would you follow it? What would you find?

____

____

____

____

____

Vocabulary

Write the correct word next to its meaning. One word will be left over.

tarry	grog	diabolical	rebuff	hawker	hamlet	indignation

1. ______ A small village
2. ______ One who sells goods aggressively by calling out
3. ______ Characteristic of a devil
4. ______ Having the characteristics of pitch or tar.
5. ______ A blunt refusal to an offer.
6. ______ Anger aroused by something unjust, mean, or untrustworthy.

After You Read

NAME: ______________________

Chapters One to Four

1. **Answer the following questions regarding the characters introduced in Chapters One and Two.**

Black Dog	Dr. Livesey	Admiral Benbow
Billy Bones	Squire Trelawney	Jim Hawkins

______ **a)** This person is the old sailor who terrorizes the inn with his songs and boisterous behavior.

______ **b)** The narrator of the story. He gets paid by Billy Bones to watch for a one-legged pirate.

______ **c)** Billy Bones threatens this man with a knife. He suggests that Billy not drink any more rum.

______ **d)** A former shipmate of Billy Bones who is missing two fingers.

______ **e)** This is one of the people who encourages Jim to write his story down.

______ **f)** The name of the inn that Jim's family owns.

Answer each question with a complete sentence.

2. Describe three things that Billy Bones does during his stay at the inn.

____

____

3. Suppose you were a friend of Jim Hawkins and you saw the one-legged man he has been looking for. Write a note to him explaining what you saw.

____

____

____

NAME: ___________________________

Chapters One to Four

Answer each question with a complete sentence.

1. How much did the old captain pay Jim to look out for the one-legged man?

____

2. What was wrong with Billy after his conversation with the two-fingered man?

____

3. What was the only possession that the old captain brought with him to the inn?

____

4. The beginning of a book or story is called the exposition. The exposition must include the Characters (Who?) and the Setting (When and Where). Based on the information that your narrator gives you, answer the following questions.

Who is involved in the story?

____

When does it take place?

____

Where does it take place?

____

5. Circle **T** if the statement is TRUE **or** **F** if it is FALSE.

- **T F** **a)** Billy asks Jim for beer after he has his stroke.
- **T F** **b)** Jim's father died.
- **T F** **c)** Jim is greeted by a deaf man at the inn.
- **T F** **d)** The man Jim speaks to is very nice to him.
- **T F** **e)** Billy's reaction to the man is welcoming.
- **T F** **f)** The pirates wanted Billy's chest.

NAME: ______________________

Chapters Five to Eight

Define the following words. Then draw a picture that represents that definition.

1. **miscreant**

Definition: ______________________

____

____

2. **cache**

Definition: ______________________

____

____

3. **Write each word next to its correct meaning. One word will be left over.**

calumnies	odious	tarpaulins	heath
dale	quid	relinquishing	

______ **a)** an extensive tract of uncultivated open land covered with herbage and low shrubs.

______ **b)** material such as waterproof canvas, used to cover and protect things from moisture.

______ **c)** a cut of chewing tobacco.

______ **d)** an empty area, a basin or valley

______ **e)** giving up or abandoning

______ **f)** arousing strong dislike or intense displeasure

Chapters Five to Eight

1. Number the events from **1** to **5** in the order they occurred.

______ **a)** Blind Pew gets run over by horses.

______ **b)** The pirates break in to the inn.

______ **c)** Pew says that the pirates could have their hands on thousands.

______ **d)** Jim leaves with Mr. Dance's company to find Dr. Livesey.

______ **e)** A gunshot disperses the pirates.

2. Draw the map that Jim found in Billy's chest. Give lots of details.

After You Read

NAME: ______________________

Chapters Five to Eight

1. The cards below have either descriptions or characters on them. Cut them out and play a memory game matching the description with who or what it is.

Hispanola	**Long John Silver**	**The ship hired to take the characters to Treasure Island**	**The man with one leg who is the cook for the Hispanola**
Dr. Livesey	**Squire Trelawney**	**The local doctor who is sailing with them to Treasure Island**	**A Bristol nobleman who arranges the trip to Treasure Island**
Spy Glass	**Tom Redruth**	**The inn where Long John Silver is staying**	**One of the sailors who assists Jim**

2. Jim is surrounded by people who have a distinctive way of speaking. Translate the following lines into everyday language.

a) "A pretty rum go if squire ain't to talk for Doctor Livesey, I should think."

____

____

b) "I had the deuce itself to find so much as a half a dozen, till the most remarkable stroke of fortune brought me the very man that I required."

____

____

c) "The score! Three goes o' rum! Why, shiver my timbers, if I hadn't forgotten my score!"

____

____

NAME: ______________________________

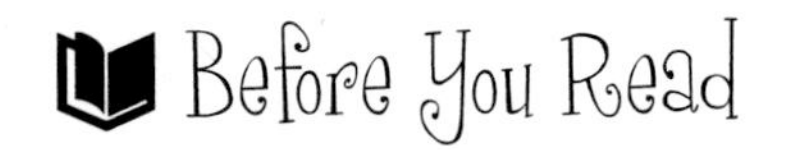

Chapters Nine to Twelve

Vocabulary

Look up the following vocabulary words. Then, put the correct word in the blank to finish the sentences. One word will be left over.

swivel	garrison	coxswain	lanyard
duff	ditty	stave	conical

1. The men on the ship sang a ____________________ of an old sea song while they cleaned the deck.
2. The captain asked the ____________________ which way was north.
3. The gym teacher dropped the whistle in his mouth making it bounce against his chest on the ____________________.
4. The campers had little to eat, but they could make ____________________ over the fire in a bag.
5. The ____________________ could move from one side to the other.
6. The soldiers stopped to rest at the ____________________ before trudging on through the woods.
7. The witch's hat was in a ____________________ shape.

8. Which answer best describes Jim Hawkins?

- ○ **A** intelligent, a good observer
- ○ **B** uninterested, bored

9. Which answer best describes John Silver?

- ○ **A** weak-minded
- ○ **B** intelligent

After You Read

NAME: ____________________

Chapters Nine to Twelve

1. Write a paragraph about the kind of first mate that Mr. Arrow turned out to be.

2. In the beginning of Chapter Nine, Captain Smollett tells Trelawney that he has several concerns about the upcoming voyage. Using complete sentences, describe at least three of his concerns.

3. What was unusual about Long John Silver's parrot?

4. In Chapter Ten, what was Captain Smollett's chief criticism of Squire Trelawney?

5. Summarize "what Jim heard in the apple barrel" (Chapter Eleven). Who was speaking? Who was he talking to? What did he say?

NAME: ___________________________

Chapters Nine to Twelve

1. Write the name of the speaker next to each statement. You may choose from the names in the box below. One name will be left over.

Jim Hawkins	Long John Silver	Captain Smollett	Squire Trelawney

a) "Now, that bird," he would say, "is, maybe, two hundred years old, Hawkins—they live forever mostly; and if anybody's seen more wickedness, it must be the devil himself. She's sailed with England, the great Cap'n England, the pirate. She's been at Madagascar, and at Malabar, and Surinam, and Providence, and Portobello. She was at the fishing up of the wrecked plate ships. It's there she learned 'Pieces of eight.'"

b) "Doctor, let me speak. Get the captain and squire down to the cabin, and then make some pretence to send for me. I have terrible news."

c) "We must go on, because we can't turn back. If I gave the word to go about, they would rise at once. Second point, we have time before us—at least until this treasure's found. Third point, there are faithful hands. Now, sir, it's got to come to blows sooner or later, and what I propose is to take time by the forelock, as the saying is, and come to blows some fine day when they least expect it. We can count, I take it, on your own home servants, Mr. Trelawney?"

2. Draw a picture showing Jim in the apple barrel and the men talking outside of it.

NAME: ________________________________

Chapters Thirteen to Fifteen

1. Match the term with its definition.

A	**becalmed**	to move with a wavelike motion	**1**
B	**scuppers**	to direct the steering of (a ship)	**2**
C	**conned**	An opening, such as a hole, gap, or slit	**3**
D	**pikes**	lack of energy or vitality	**4**
E	**undulating**	To render motionless for lack of wind	**5**
F	**fen**	weapons consisting of a metal spearhead on a long wooden shaft	**6**
G	**aperture**	openings in the sides of the ship that allow water to run off the deck	**7**
H	**modulated**	Low, flat, swampy land; a bog or marsh	**8**
I	**nondescript**	a supernatural appearance of a person or thing	**9**
J	**apparition**	inappropriate; unbecoming	**10**
K	**incongruous**	Lacking distinctive qualities; having no individual character or form	**11**
L	**gaskin**	soften; tone down.	**12**
M	**languor**	a legging or gaiter (a cloth or leather covering for the instep and ankle).	**13**

2. Have you ever thought about being on a desert island? How do you think you'd feel? What do you think you'd see?

____

____

____

____

NAME: ______________________________

Chapters Thirteen to Fifteen

Put a check mark (✓) next to the answer that is most correct.

1. The general coloring of the island was:

- ◯ **A** bright and cheerful
- ◯ **B** black and frightening
- ◯ **C** uniform and sad

2. How had the sight of the island affected the crew?

- ◯ **A** They were excited about going ashore.
- ◯ **B** They became undisciplined.
- ◯ **C** They hid away in terror.

3. Who did Jim find on the island?

- ◯ **A** Long John Silver
- ◯ **B** Captain Smollett
- ◯ **C** Squire Trelawney

4. What did Silver do to Tom?

- ◯ **A** He shot him.
- ◯ **B** He strangled him.
- ◯ **C** He threw his crutch at his back.

5. Who did Jim meet as he ran away from Silver?

- ◯ **A** Dr. Livesey
- ◯ **B** Ben Gunn
- ◯ **C** Silver himself

After You Read

NAME: ____________________

Chapters Thirteen to Fifteen

1. Circle **T** if the statement is TRUE **or** **F** if it is FALSE.

T F **a)** The ship's name was the Bismarck.

T F **b)** The captain knew that Jim was going to sneak ashore.

T F **c)** Ben Gunn had been on the island three years.

T F **d)** Ben asked Jim if he happened to have a bit of bread with him.

T F **e)** Billy Bones was the first mate on Flint's old ship.

2. Describe the plan that Jim and Ben made to get back to the ship without Long John Silver noticing them.

____

____

____

____

3. Describe Ben Gunn. How did he get to the island? What kind of man was he? What did he tell Jim?

____

____

____

____

NAME: ______________________

Chapters Sixteen to Eighteen

Choose one word from the box to complete each sentence.

abominable	stockade	gig	cognac	palisade
jolly-boat	gallipot	contrived		

1. ______________ food is very unpleasant or disagreeable.
2. A ______________ is a small pot or jar of glazed earthenware, especially one used by druggists as a container for medicine.
3. An action that is ______________ is obviously planned or forced.
4. A ______________ is an enclosure or pen made with posts and stakes.
5. A long, light ship's boat is called a ______________.
6. A sailing vessel's small boat, usually carried on the stern is called a __________-__________.
7. A merchant might sip French brandy or ______________.
8. A ______________ is a fence of stakes set firmly in the ground.

9. The years from 1715 to 1725 have been called the "Golden Age of Piracy". Choose one of the pirates listed below and write a short essay about his/her life.

Stede Bonnet	Anne Bonny	William Kidd	Jean Laffite
Henry Morgan	Edward Teach	Mary Read	

____

____

____

____

____

____

After You Read

NAME: ______________________

Chapters Sixteen to Eighteen

1. Write the name of the speaker next to each statement. You may choose from the names in the box below.

Jim Hawkins	Captain Smollett	Long John Silver
The Doctor	Squire Trelawney	Ben Gunn

a) "Gray, I am leaving this ship, and I order you to follow your captain. I know you are a good man at bottom, and I dare say not one of the lot of you's as bad as he makes out. I have my watch here in my hand; I give you thirty seconds to join me in." (Chapter 16)

b) "Captain," said I, "Trelawney is the dead shot. Give him your gun; his own is useless." (Chapter 18)

c) "Mr. Trelawney, will you please pick me off one of these men, sir? Hands, if possible," (Chapter 17)

d) Who was the person telling the story in Chapters 16, 17, and 18?

e) Who did the doctor see climbing over the stockade at the end of Chapter 18?

2. What is a stockade that was mentioned in Chapter 16?

____

____

____

____

NAME: ______________________

Chapters Sixteen to Eighteen

Crossword Puzzle

Word List
- apparition
- Benbow
- Bones
- buccaneer
- Captain
- chest
- fen
- Gunn
- Jim Hawkins
- Livesey
- Long John
- oilcloth
- pirate
- treasure

Across

1. Admiral ________ Inn
3. The innkeeper's son ___ ________
4. Doctor ____________
5. _____ _____ Silver
6. ____________ Smollet
8. another word for "pirate"
9. 15 men on a dead man's ______

Down

1. Billy ______
2. cloth treated to make it waterproof
3. a supernatural appearance of a person or thing
7. Ben ______
8. Blackbeard was a __________
9. Low, swampy land
10. Buried __________

NAME: ______________________________

Chapters Nineteen to Twenty-one

Put a check mark (✓) next to the answer that is most correct.

1. "Placidly" means

- ○ **A** pleasantly calm
- ○ **B** agitated
- ○ **C** dangerous

2. "Avast" means

- ○ **A** hurry up
- ○ **B** stop
- ○ **C** pay attention

3. "Drub" means

- ○ **A** to laugh
- ○ **B** to defeat decisively
- ○ **C** to take care of

4. "Girdle" means

- ○ **A** a belt or sash worn around the waist
- ○ **B** a tight-fitting shirt
- ○ **C** a kind of ladies' shoe

5. "Hurly-burly" means

- ○ **A** a peaceful scene
- ○ **B** a kind of dance
- ○ **C** commotion, confusion

6. "Hanger" means

- ○ **A** a large saber
- ○ **B** a place to store cars
- ○ **C** an earring

7. "Sallied" means

- ○ **A** crept along quietly
- ○ **B** burst forth to attack an enemy.
- ○ **C** talked slowly

Chapters Nineteen to Twenty-one

1. Number the events from **1** to **6** in the order they occurred.

_____ **a)** Jim finds the Captain and the others in the stockade.

_____ **b)** Silver tells the Captain that he wants the treasure.

_____ **c)** Jim and the others fight the mutineers.

_____ **d)** Ben Gunn boards the ship for the first time.

_____ **e)** Silver comes to the stockade under a flag of truce.

_____ **f)** The Captain is angry because Gray is the only man at his post.

Write a short answer to each question.

2. In Chapter 19, how did Ben Gunn know that the Captain was still in charge of the ship?

____

____

3. What did Ben Gunn mean when he said, "And if them pirates camp ashore, Jim, what would you say but there'd be widders (widows) in the morning?"

____

____

4. Describe the pirates' attack on the stockade.

____

____

5. Name some of the weapons mentioned in Chapters 19, 20, and 21.

____

____

After You Read

NAME: ______________________________

Chapters Nineteen to Twenty-one

Who Said It? Put a check mark (✓) beside the name of the speaker for each quotation.

1. "Well, Jim," says he, "just see the good that comes of being dainty in your food. You've seen my snuff-box, haven't you? And you never saw me take snuff, the reason being that in my snuff-box I carry a piece of Parmesan cheese—a cheese made in Italy, very nutritious. Well, that's for Ben Gunn!"

- ◯ Captain Smollett
- ◯ the Doctor
- ◯ Long John Silver

2. "First ship that ever I lost."

- ◯ Squire Trelawney
- ◯ Jim Hawkins
- ◯ Captain Smollett

3. "We want that treasure, and we'll have it—that's our point! You would just as soon save your lives, I reckon; and that's yours. You have a chart, haven't you?"

- ◯ Jim Hawkins
- ◯ Long John Silver
- ◯ Ben Gunn

4. "Who'll give me a hand up?"

- ◯ Long John Silver
- ◯ Jim Hawkins
- ◯ the Squire

5. Who were the honest people in the story?

____

____

____

NAME: ______________________________

Chapters Twenty-two to Twenty-four

1. Put the letter of each word before its definition.

	Word		Definition	
A	**plaster**	___	worked	1
B	**girt**	___	the act of being repelled as in a battle	2
C	**brace**	___	causing fear, apprehension, or dread:	3
D	**crags**	___	a short, simple song	4
E	**spit**	___	a short, roundish boat of skins or waterproofed canvas stretched over a wood or wicker frame.	5
F	**formidable**	___	A steep rugged mass of rock projecting upward or outward.	6
G	**thwart**	___	a knife, especially, a large kitchen or butcher knife.	7
H	**coracle**	___	a seat across a boat, especially one used by a rower	8
I	**repulse**	___	a heavy rope for mooring or towing	9
J	**hawser**	___	a narrow point of land projecting into the water	10
K	**gully**	___	a pair	11
L	**ditty**	___	To encircle with a belt or band	12
M	**wrought**	___	a solid or semisolid preparation spread upon cloth, plastic, or other material and applied to the body, especially for some healing purpose	13

After You Read

NAME: ______________________________

Chapters Twenty-two to Twenty-four

Short Answer **Write the answer to each question in the blank.**

1. Describe the Captain's injuries from the battle with Long John Silver and the other pirates.

____

____

2. To what did Jim compare his injury?

____

3. What did Jim call Ben Gunn's homemade boat?

____

4. What did Jim see when he climbed up to the cabin window and looked in?

____

____

5. What kind of animals did Jim describe as "huge, slimy monsters"?

____

6. Draw a picture of Jim in the coracle as he spots the Hispaniola. Include details of both boats that you can find in Chapter 24.

NAME: ______________________________

After You Read

Chapters Twenty-two to Twenty-four

1. Circle **T** if the statement is TRUE **or** **F** if it is FALSE.

T	**F**	**a)** Jim and the Squire were afraid to cook outside after the pirates' attack ended.
T	**F**	**b)** The Captain's wounds were not very dangerous.
T	**F**	**c)** Jim ran away from the stockade.
T	**F**	**d)** The Jolly Roger was not flying from the flagpole on the Hispaniola.
T	**F**	**e)** Ben Gunn had made the coracle.
T	**F**	**f)** A hawser is a thin rope tied to a boat.

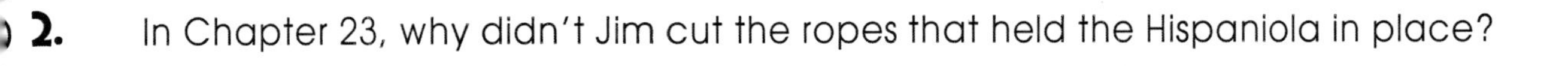

2. In Chapter 23, why didn't Jim cut the ropes that held the Hispaniola in place?

____

____

3. What did Jim mean when he said, "But, indeed, from what I saw, all these buccaneers were as callous as the sea they sailed on," in Chapter 23? (You may use the dictionary to help you.)

____

____

4. Why do you think Chapter 24 is named "The Cruise of the Coracle"?

____

____

5. What kind of situation was Jim in at the end of Chapter 24?

____

____

Before You Read

NAME: ______________________

Chapters Twenty-five to Twenty-seven

1. Write the correct term in front of its definition.

foraging	jib	gill	canted	red ensign
mizzen shrouds	younker	tremulous	dirk	

a) a long, straight dagger

b) a youngster

c) a unit of liquid measure equal to ¼ pint or 4 fluid ounces

d) characterized by trembling, as from fear, nervousness, or weakness

e) the ropes stretched from the ship's side to the head of the mizzenmast to offset lateral strain on the mast

f) a triangular sail secured to a stay forward of the foremast.

g) red flag or banner

h) to wander or go in search of provisions (food)

i) to lean to one side

2. Use the space below to write a newspaper story about one of Jim's adventures we have read about in the book thus far. Remember the "who", "what", "where", "when", and "why" of good reporting.

Headline: ______________________

NAME: ______________________

Chapters Twenty-five to Twenty-seven

1. The title of Chapter 25 is "I Strike the Jolly Roger". In the space below draw a picture of the Jolly Roger as it flew from the "Hispaniola".

2. How did Jim Hawkins get to be captain of the "Hispaniola" in Chapter 25?

____

____

____

3. Who was Israel Hands and what happened between Jim and him?

____

____

4. What does Jim mean in Chapter 27 when he says, "Ben Gunn – the maroon"?

____

____

5. What are "pieces of eight" and who or what kept shouting about them?

____

____

After You Read

NAME: ____________________

Chapters Twenty-five to Twenty-seven

1. Number the events from 1 to 4 in the order they occurred.

______ **a)** Jim meets Long John's parrot and tries to run away from the pirates.

______ **b)** Hands attacks Jim with his dirk.

______ **c)** Jim shoots Hands with his pistols.

______ **d)** Jim takes down the Jolly Roger flag.

2. What did Jim do with the pirate named O'Brien? Why?

____

____

3. Who did Jim meet just after he roused the parrot, Captain Flint?

____

____

4. **Suppose that you have been asked to illustrate the last scene in Chapter 27 for a new printing of *Treasure Island*. Take a few minutes to plan your drawing and then sketch it below.**

NAME: ______________________________

Chapters Twenty-eight to Thirty-one

1. Match each term with its meaning.

1	**link**	a small portion, a scrap (of wood)	A
2	**smote**	to fasten canvas over a ship's hatchways (covered openings in the deck) as in preparing for a storm; here Silver simply means "shut your mouth."	B
3	**glim**	to affect mentally or morally with a sudden pang	C
4	**truculently**	a representative sent on a mission or errand	D
5	**puncheon**	surrounded	E
6	**apprehensions**	a torch made of pitch	F
7	**batten down your hatches**	disease-bearing swamp or swamp-like region.	G
8	**emissary**	brutally harsh	H
9	**hornpipe**	salted port or beef	I
10	**environed**	uneasy anticipations of the future	J
11	**pestiferous slough**	a rum cask	K
12	**slip your cable**	a plant that grows upon or just beneath the surface of the ground	L
13	**fried junk**	a lively, jig-like dance (according to Silver - at the end of a rope)	M
14	**slow-growing creeper**	tobacco box	N
15	**baccy box**	escape	O

NAME: ______________________________

Chapters Twenty-eight to Thirty-one

Who Said It? **Put a check mark (✓) beside the name of the speaker for each quotation.**

1. "So," said he, "here's Jim Hawkins, shiver my timbers! Dropped in, like, eh? Well, come, I take that friendly."

- ○ the Doctor
- ○ Long John Silver
- ○ Dick

2. "Let the worst come to the worst, it's little I care. I've seen too many die since I fell in with you."

- ○ Jim Hawkins
- ○ Long John Silver
- ○ the Captain

3. "It'll do to kiss the book on still, won't it?"

- ○ Long John Silver
- ○ Jim
- ○ Dick

4. "Well, well," he said at last, "duty first and pleasure afterwards, as you might have said yourself, Silver. Let us overhaul these patients of yours."

- ○ The Doctor
- ○ Jim
- ○ Long John Silver

5. "I seen the doctor waving you to run for it—with the tail of my eye, I did; and I seen you say no, as plain as hearing."

- ○ the Captain
- ○ Morgan
- ○ Long John Silver

NAME: ______________________________

Chapters Twenty-eight to Thirty-one

Answer the questions in complete sentences.

1. What is a "forecastle council"?

____

____

2. When the pirates return to Silver, what do they give him?

____

3. What was written on it and what did it mean?

____

____

4. What did Silver do after the men gave him the black spot?

____

____

5. Write the name of each character being described beside the correct description.

Jim Hawkins	Dr. Livesey	Long John Silver	Morgan	Dick	George Merry

______ **a)** This person believes in the Rules of Piracy and challenges Silver to a "forecastle council". He also has a liver condition and has turned a "pretty color".

______ **b)** This person told all the pirates that they were suffering from malaria. He also tried to get Jim to run away from Long John Silver.

______ **c)** The pirates call this man "Barbeque".

______ **d)** This person cut up a Bible and was afraid that he was cursed because of his actions.

NAME: ______________________________

Chapters Thirty-two to Thirty-four

1. Write the correct word next to its definition.

plateau	skylarking	precipice	volubly	conspicuous	countenance	underwood
cache	prodigious	imposter	dereliction	obsequious	palisade	formidable

[ ] **a)** deliberate or conscious neglect

[ ] **b)** easily seen or noticed

[ ] **c)** playing actively and loudly

[ ] **d)** of great strength; forceful; powerful

[ ] **e)** a person who pretends to be someone or something that he is not.

[ ] **f)** a hiding place for treasure

[ ] **g)** appearance

[ ] **h)** overhanging or extremely steep mass of rock

2. Use a word from the box above to complete each sentence.

a) It was easy for Jim to run across the ____________________, which was flat, level land.

b) Long John Silver was being ____________________ since it was obvious that he was trying to get on the Captain's good side by flattering him.

c) Jim and the other seamen built a fence of wooden stakes called a ____________________ around the hut.

d) Long John Silver's desire for pirate's treasure was ____________________ or far beyond what is considered normal.

e) Ben Gunn spoke ____________________ or continuously throughout the night.

NAME: ______________________________

Chapters Thirty-two to Thirty-four

Answer each question in a complete sentence.

1. At first, whose voice did Silver and the other pirates think they were hearing?

____

2. What were Jim, Long John Silver, and the others searching for when they heard the voice in the trees?

____

____

3. Who found the packing cases with the name, "WALRUS", written on them?

____

4. What was the significance of this name?

____

____

5. What startling information is revealed at the end of Chapter 32?

____

____

6. Explain what the author meant when he wrote, "There never was such an overturn in this world," at the beginning of Chapter 33.

____

____

7. What happened to George Merry as he and Silver argued about the disappearance of the gold?

____

____

8. Explain what the Squire meant when he told Long John Silver that, "the dead men, sir, hang about your neck like mill-stones."

____

____

NAME: ____________________

Chapters Thirty-two to Thirty-four

Answer each question in a complete sentence.

9. Who and what did Jim, Silver, and the doctor find when they finally entered a cave that was, "a large, airy place, with a little spring and a pool of clear water, overhung with ferns."

____

____

10. Read the third paragraph of Chapter 34 and then write a description of what Jim found in the cave.

____

____

The End of the Matter

11. Write at least two paragraphs telling what happened after Jim and the Doctor heard the voices of the pirates who had run away from them and Long John Silver. How does the book end?

____

____

____

____

____

____

12. What happened to Ben Gunn?

____

____

13. What does Jim mean when he writes that Long John Silver's "chances of comfort in another world are very small."

____

____

Imagine that you are Jim after he leaves Treasure Island and arrives on the island with the friendly natives in Chapter 34. Write a letter home to mother and give her a good idea of what you've been doing all this time.

The song, "Fifteen Men on a Dead Man's Chest", is mentioned throughout Treasure Island. Try your hand at songwriting and compose a "ditty" about the people and events of this book. Write the words on your own paper. You may want to use the tune to another song that's familiar to your friends.

Imagine that *Treasure Island* is being made into a movie again. Write a radio announcement that will make people want to see the movie. Who will be the stars? Where do you think it should be made?

Writing Task #4

Who are the main characters in *Treasure Island*? Write at least two paragraphs telling what you think each one would be doing ten years after they left the island. Use descriptive language as much as possible.

Writing Task #5

Use your dictionary to define the word "hero." Could any of the characters in the book be described as heroes? Justify your answer.

Writing Task #6

Jim Hawkins is the main character in *Treasure Island*. Which character has the biggest influence (good or bad) on him? Describe their relationship and how it affects the outcome of the story.

NAME: ____________________

Word Search

Find all of the words in the Word Search. Words may be horizontal, vertical or even diagonal. A few may even be backwards. Look carefully!

Admiral Benbow	Captain Smollett	Fifteen Men	Map	Skeleton
Ben Gunn	Coins	Gold	Parrot	Squire Trelawney
Billy Bones	Dead Man's Chest	Jolly Roger	Pieces of Eight	Stevenson
Bottle of Rum	Doctor Livesey	Jim Hawkins	Pirates	Stockade
Buccaneer	England	Long John Silver	Robert Louis	Treasure Island

c	v	a	r	l	y	t	a	e	u	q	g	a	s	m	f	f	y	c	i	j	g
n	o	s	t	r	e	a	s	u	r	e	i	s	l	a	n	d	e	c	e	a	s
i	r	n	n	n	d	i	r	u	m	i	r	a	c	p	e	u	n	a	r	i	l
t	s	i	t	k	r	a	b	e	n	g	u	n	n	v	c	f	w	p	e	n	d
b	e	k	i	a	v	o	r	y	i	g	l	a	z	e	o	p	a	t	d	y	b
e	j	w	o	b	n	e	b	l	a	r	i	m	d	a	i	u	l	a	s	y	n
h	u	a	b	l	e	c	f	e	n	g	l	a	n	d	n	e	e	i	k	o	n
l	s	h	a	h	b	n	f	a	r	r	t	r	g	o	s	l	r	n	e	s	u
o	e	m	r	d	e	u	e	t	a	t	t	e	p	d	n	i	t	s	l	m	v
u	p	i	r	a	t	e	s	i	p	r	l	n	l	o	o	j	e	m	e	i	c
s	i	j	w	t	s	i	n	n	s	a	c	o	r	p	a	r	r	o	t	r	m
l	r	d	s	a	e	y	f	c	g	b	g	r	u	o	m	e	i	l	o	t	p
c	h	j	o	l	l	y	r	o	g	e	r	r	r	i	s	v	u	l	n	v	i
a	s	e	m	d	s	e	n	o	b	y	l	l	i	b	s	l	q	e	t	r	v
i	m	p	i	e	c	e	s	o	f	e	i	g	h	t	s	i	s	t	c	t	s
h	n	i	l	a	c	v	m	t	f	s	c	o	i	p	m	s	n	t	d	a	t
i	n	o	v	d	d	l	a	e	e	y	n	u	a	g	d	n	n	d	e	i	o
i	n	h	t	m	s	h	e	e	p	v	v	j	n	i	m	h	c	x	z	o	c
b	u	c	c	a	n	e	e	r	t	i	e	b	t	u	i	o	b	v	c	o	k
a	s	r	g	n	i	o	l	m	n	y	g	n	p	g	h	j	u	k	w	f	a
f	v	h	m	s	o	g	b	y	b	u	m	n	s	a	t	g	y	u	j	k	d
g	f	s	a	c	m	u	r	f	o	e	l	t	t	o	b	n	h	j	h	m	e
h	t	j	k	h	s	a	e	e	r	t	u	i	o	m	n	o	j	f	r	e	e
y	j	d	a	e	q	v	z	m	k	i	i	e	a	k	l	l	m	a	s	f	g
z	b	c	s	s	d	o	c	t	o	r	l	i	v	e	s	e	y	l	q	b	m
i	r	t	p	t	e	r	t	n	e	m	n	e	e	t	f	i	f	p	x	n	j

NAME: ______________________

Comprehension Quiz

25

Answer each question in a complete sentence or short paragraph.

1. Who was the narrator of most of Treasure Island? In Chapter One, why does he say that he's writing the story?

____

______________________ 2

2. What part of the adventure did the writer leave out and why?

____

______________________ 2

3. In Chapter Two, how did Billy Bones react when he saw the stranger he called "Black Dog"? 1

____

4. What did Pew and the others want from Billy Bones's sea chest and who finally got it?

____

______________________ 2

5. After Jim takes the papers from the chest to Doctor Livesey and the Squire, what do they decide to do?

____

______________________ 1

6. What was the most important paper from the sea chest? 1

____

7. Who was hired as the cook for the voyage? 1

____

8. Describe the appearances of the seamen that the Squire interviewed. (Ch. 7)

____

______________________ 2

SUBTOTAL: /12

After You Read

NAME: ____________________

Comprehension Quiz

9. Describe Long John Silver. (Chapter 8)

____

____

(2)

10. How did Captain Smollett feel about the first mate and the sailors that the Squire hired?

____

(1)

11. What was the name of the ship Jim and the others sailed on and who was the first mate?

____

____

(2)

12. Who or what was Long John Silver's constant companion?

____

(1)

13. What happened to the first mate?

____

(1)

14. Where was Jim when he overheard Silver and the others talking about mutiny?

____

(1)

15. In Chapter 14, Jim calls Long John Silver a "monster". Why do you believe he did this?

____

____

(2)

16. Which character found Flint's treasure first?

____

(1)

17. Where did the first battle between Silver's pirates and Jim and his friends happen?

____

(1)

18. Why did Long John Silver visit Captain Smollett in the stockade?

____

(1)

SUBTOTAL: /13

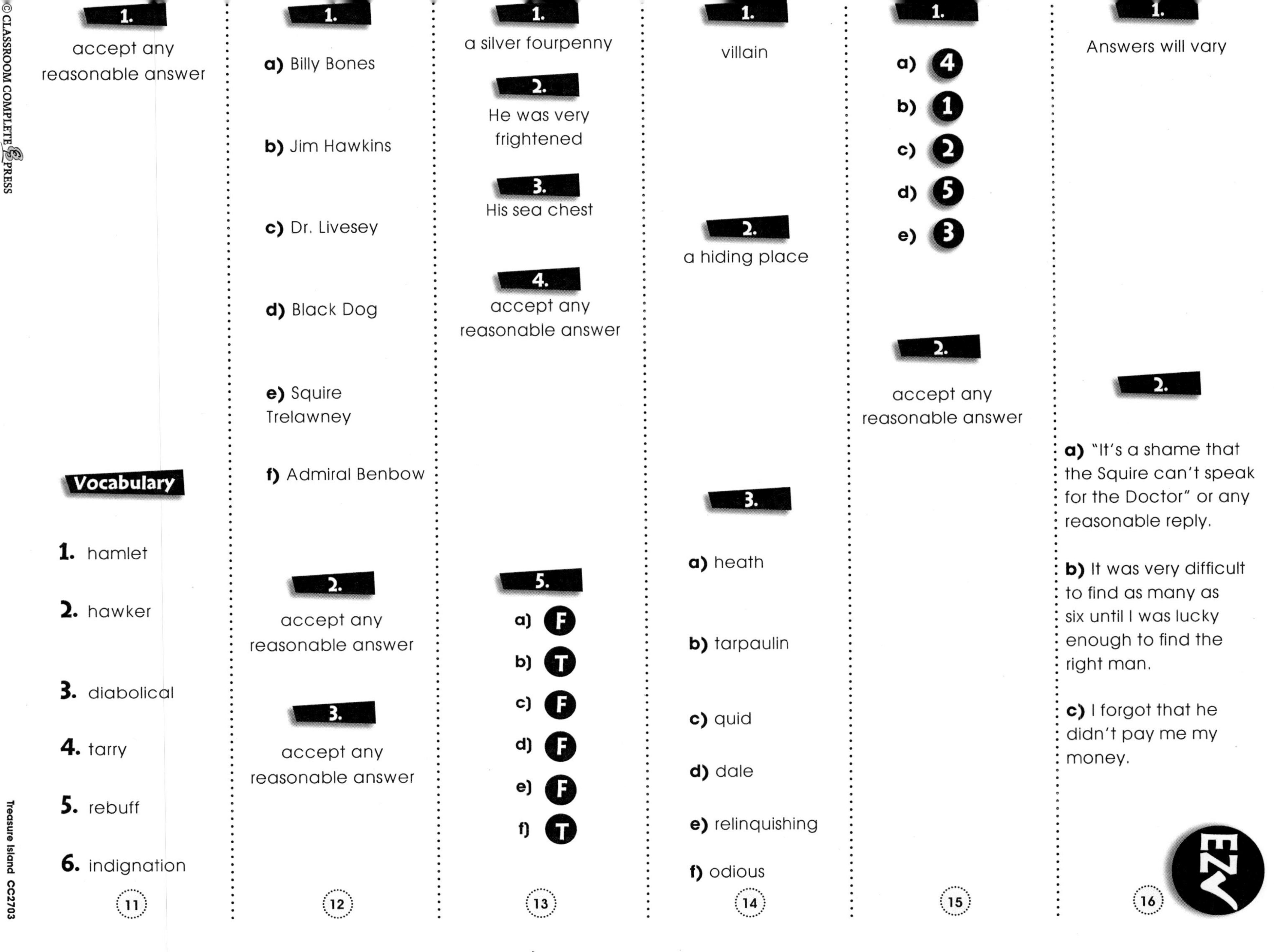

1. accept any reasonable answer

Vocabulary

1. hamlet
2. hawker
3. diabolical
4. tarry
5. rebuff
6. indignation

11

1.
- **a)** Billy Bones
- **b)** Jim Hawkins
- **c)** Dr. Livesey
- **d)** Black Dog
- **e)** Squire Trelawney
- **f)** Admiral Benbow

2. accept any reasonable answer

3. accept any reasonable answer

12

1. a silver fourpenny

2. He was very frightened

3. His sea chest

4. accept any reasonable answer

5.
- a) F
- b) T
- c) F
- d) F
- e) F
- f) T

13

1. villain

2. a hiding place

3.
- **a)** heath
- **b)** tarpaulin
- **c)** quid
- **d)** dale
- **e)** relinquishing
- **f)** odious

14

1.
- **a)** 4
- **b)** 1
- **c)** 2
- **d)** 5
- **e)** 3

2. accept any reasonable answer

15

1. Answers will vary

2.
- **a)** "It's a shame that the Squire can't speak for the Doctor" or any reasonable reply.
- **b)** It was very difficult to find as many as six until I was lucky enough to find the right man.
- **c)** I forgot that he didn't pay me my money.

16

EZ✓

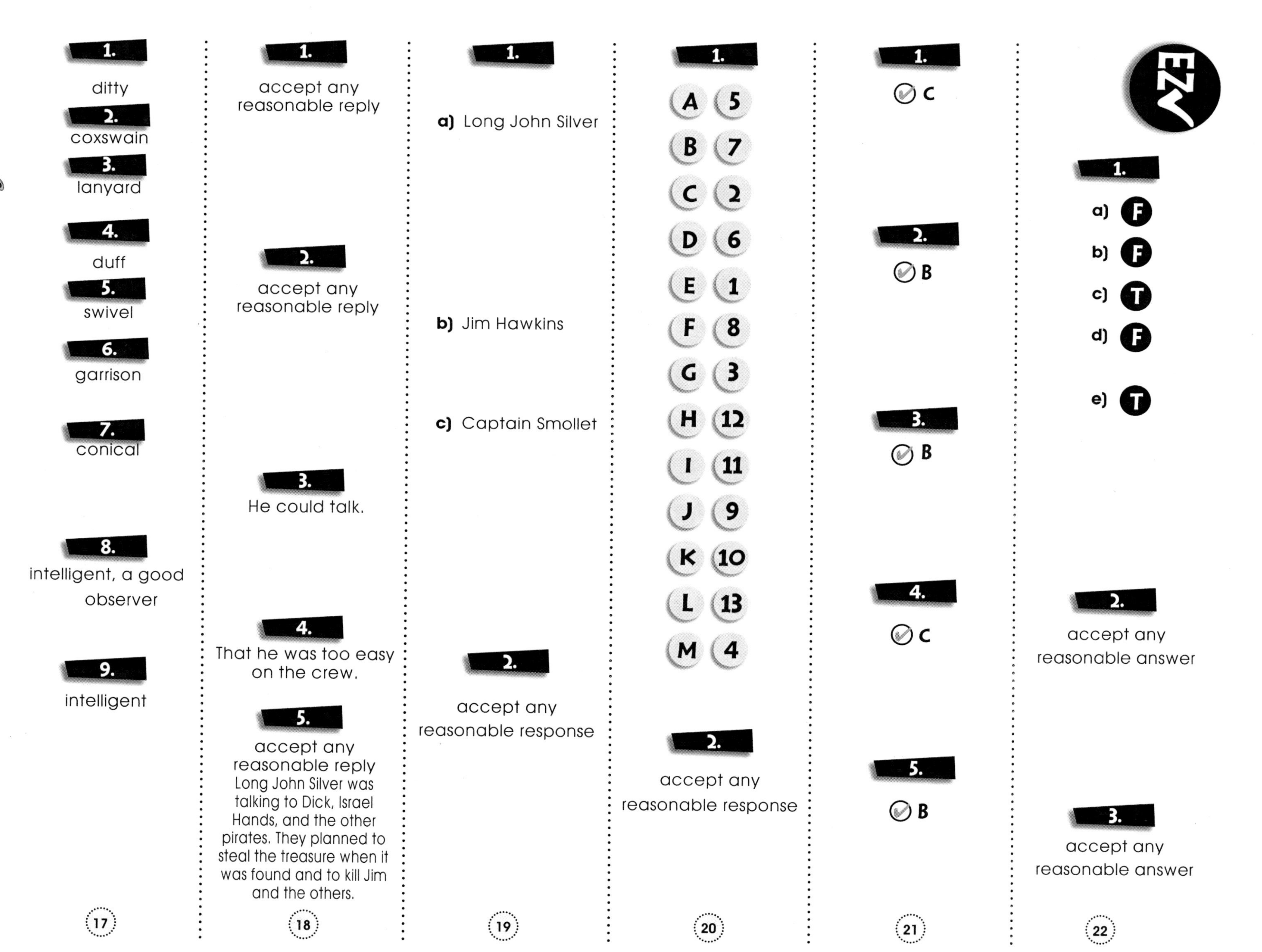

Page 17

1. ditty
2. coxswain
3. lanyard
4. duff
5. swivel
6. garrison
7. conical
8. intelligent, a good observer
9. intelligent

Page 18

1. accept any reasonable reply
2. accept any reasonable reply
3. He could talk.
4. That he was too easy on the crew.
5. accept any reasonable reply
Long John Silver was talking to Dick, Israel Hands, and the other pirates. They planned to steal the treasure when it was found and to kill Jim and the others.

Page 19

1. a) Long John Silver
b) Jim Hawkins
c) Captain Smollet
2. accept any reasonable response

Page 20

1. A 5, B 7, C 2, D 6, E 1, F 8, G 3, H 12, I 11, J 9, K 10, L 13, M 4
2. accept any reasonable response

Page 21

1. C
2. B
3. B
4. C
5. B

Page 22

EZ✓

1. a) F
b) F
c) T
d) F
e) T
2. accept any reasonable answer
3. accept any reasonable answer

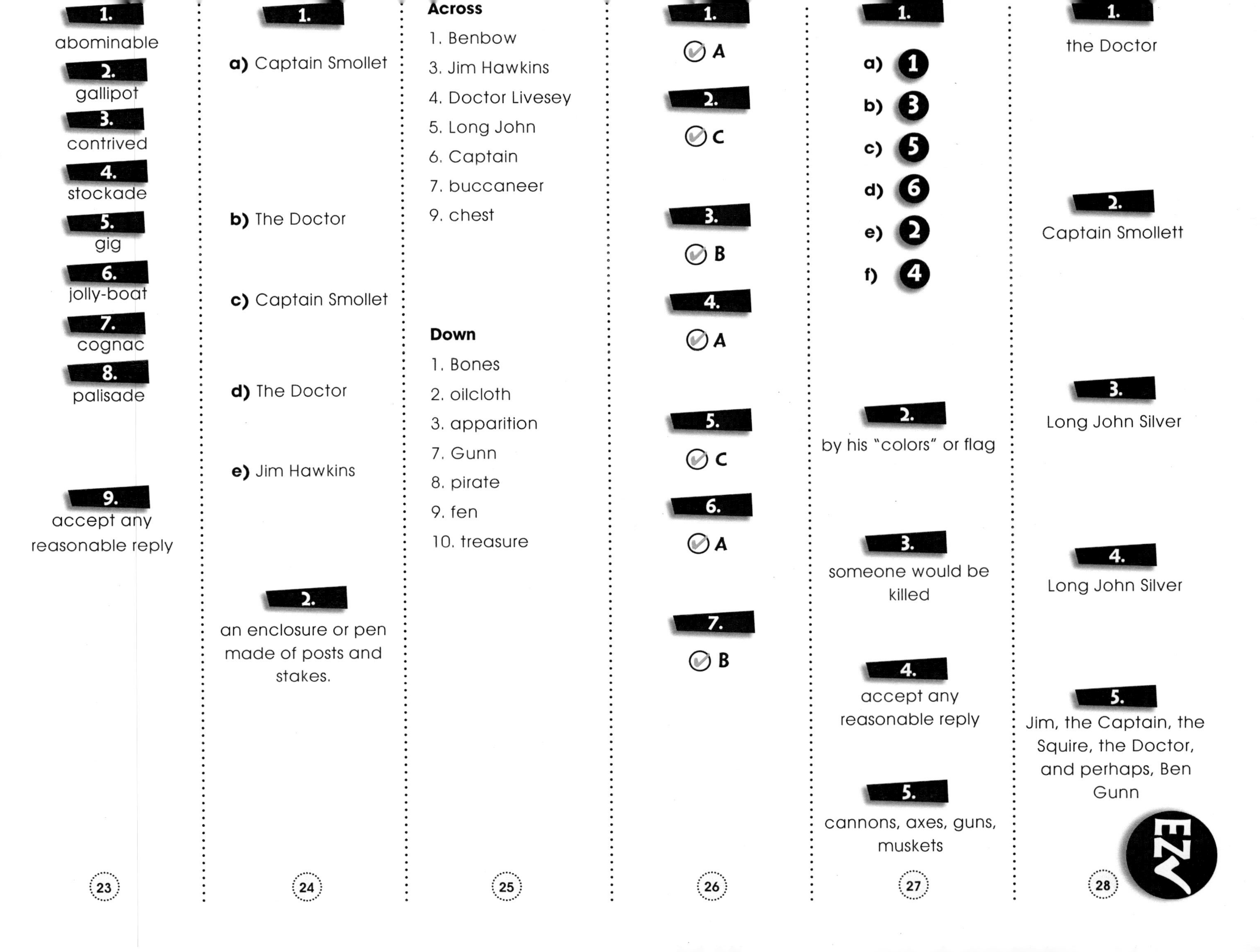

1. abominable

2. gallipot

3. contrived

4. stockade

5. gig

6. jolly-boat

7. cognac

8. palisade

9. accept any reasonable reply

(23)

1.

a) Captain Smollet

b) The Doctor

c) Captain Smollet

d) The Doctor

e) Jim Hawkins

2. an enclosure or pen made of posts and stakes.

(24)

Across

1. Benbow
3. Jim Hawkins
4. Doctor Livesey
5. Long John
6. Captain
7. buccaneer
9. chest

Down

1. Bones
2. oilcloth
3. apparition
7. Gunn
8. pirate
9. fen
10. treasure

(25)

1. ✓ A

2. ✓ C

3. ✓ B

4. ✓ A

5. ✓ C

6. ✓ A

7. ✓ B

(26)

1.

a) 1

b) 3

c) 5

d) 6

e) 2

f) 4

2. by his "colors" or flag

3. someone would be killed

4. accept any reasonable reply

5. cannons, axes, guns, muskets

(27)

1. the Doctor

2. Captain Smollett

3. Long John Silver

4. Long John Silver

5. Jim, the Captain, the Squire, the Doctor, and perhaps, Ben Gunn

(28)

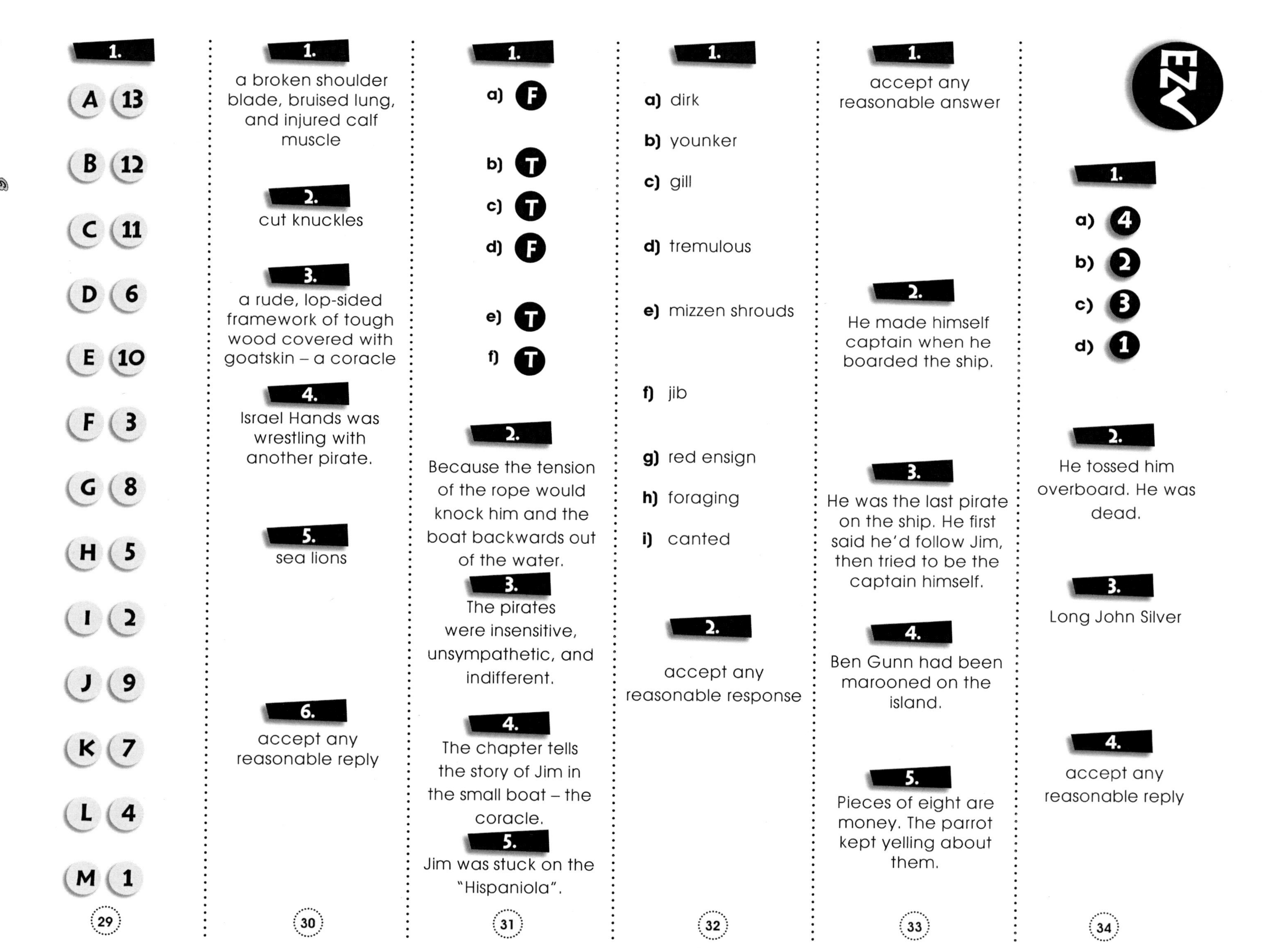

EZ✓

Page 29

1.

- A 13
- B 12
- C 11
- D 6
- E 10
- F 3
- G 8
- H 5
- I 2
- J 9
- K 7
- L 4
- M 1

Page 30

1. a broken shoulder blade, bruised lung, and injured calf muscle

2. cut knuckles

3. a rude, lop-sided framework of tough wood covered with goatskin – a coracle

4. Israel Hands was wrestling with another pirate.

5. sea lions

6. accept any reasonable reply

Page 31

1.

- a) F
- b) T
- c) T
- d) F
- e) T
- f) T

2. Because the tension of the rope would knock him and the boat backwards out of the water.

3. The pirates were insensitive, unsympathetic, and indifferent.

4. The chapter tells the story of Jim in the small boat – the coracle.

5. Jim was stuck on the "Hispaniola".

Page 32

1.

- a) dirk
- b) younker
- c) gill
- d) tremulous
- e) mizzen shrouds
- f) jib
- g) red ensign
- h) foraging
- i) canted

2. accept any reasonable response

Page 33

1. accept any reasonable answer

2. He made himself captain when he boarded the ship.

3. He was the last pirate on the ship. He first said he'd follow Jim, then tried to be the captain himself.

4. Ben Gunn had been marooned on the island.

5. Pieces of eight are money. The parrot kept yelling about them.

Page 34

1.

- a) 4
- b) 2
- c) 3
- d) 1

2. He tossed him overboard. He was dead.

3. Long John Silver

4. accept any reasonable reply

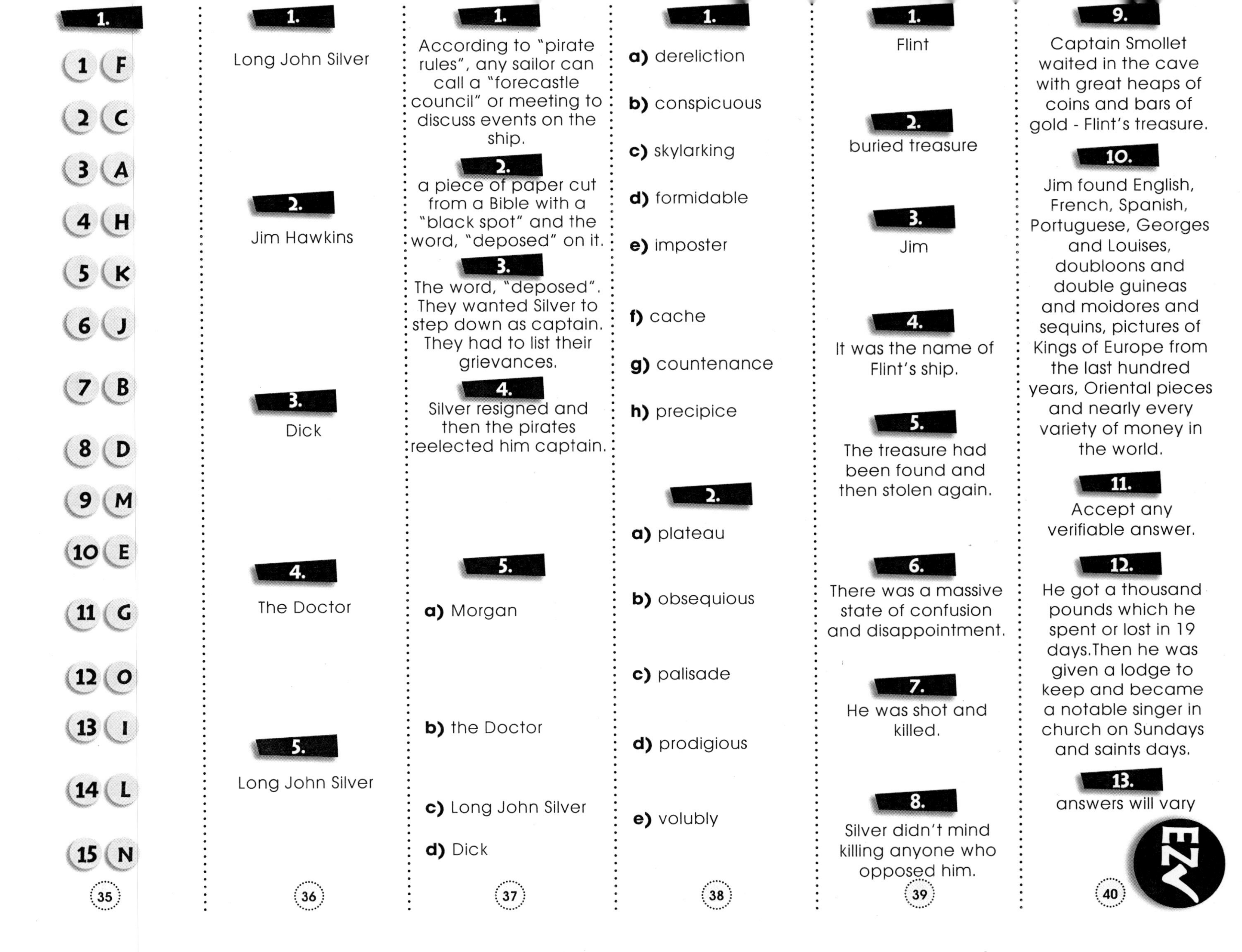

1.

1 F
2 C
3 A
4 H
5 K
6 J
7 B
8 D
9 M
10 E
11 G
12 O
13 I
14 L
15 N

(35)

---

1. Long John Silver

2. Jim Hawkins

3. Dick

4. The Doctor

5. Long John Silver

(36)

---

1. According to "pirate rules", any sailor can call a "forecastle council" or meeting to discuss events on the ship.

2. a piece of paper cut from a Bible with a "black spot" and the word, "deposed" on it.

3. The word, "deposed". They wanted Silver to step down as captain. They had to list their grievances.

4. Silver resigned and then the pirates reelected him captain.

5.

a) Morgan

b) the Doctor

c) Long John Silver

d) Dick

(37)

1.

a) dereliction

b) conspicuous

c) skylarking

d) formidable

e) imposter

f) cache

g) countenance

h) precipice

2.

a) plateau

b) obsequious

c) palisade

d) prodigious

e) volubly

(38)

---

1. Flint

2. buried treasure

3. Jim

4. It was the name of Flint's ship.

5. The treasure had been found and then stolen again.

6. There was a massive state of confusion and disappointment.

7. He was shot and killed.

8. Silver didn't mind killing anyone who opposed him.

(39)

---

9. Captain Smollet waited in the cave with great heaps of coins and bars of gold - Flint's treasure.

10. Jim found English, French, Spanish, Portuguese, Georges and Louises, doubloons and double guineas and moidores and sequins, pictures of Kings of Europe from the last hundred years, Oriental pieces and nearly every variety of money in the world.

11. Accept any verifiable answer.

12. He got a thousand pounds which he spent or lost in 19 days.Then he was given a lodge to keep and became a notable singer in church on Sundays and saints days.

13. answers will vary

EZ✓

(40)

Word Search Answers

c	v	a	r	l	y	t	a	e	u	q	g	a	s	m	f	f	y	c	i	j	g
n	o	s	t	r	e	a	s	u	r	e	i	s	l	a	n	d	e	c	e	a	s
i	r	n	n	n	d	i	r	u	m	i	r	a	c	p	e	u	n	a	r	i	l
t	s	i	t	k	r	a	b	e	n	g	u	n	n	v	c	f	w	p	e	n	d
b	e	k	i	a	v	o	r	y	i	g	l	a	z	e	o	p	a	t	d	y	b
e	j	w	o	b	n	e	b	l	a	r	i	m	d	a	i	u	l	a	s	y	n
h	u	a	b	l	e	c	f	e	n	g	l	a	n	d	n	e	e	i	k	o	n
l	s	h	a	h	b	n	f	d	r	r	t	r	g	o	s	l	r	n	e	s	u
o	e	m	r	d	e	u	e	t	a	t	t	e	p	a	n	i	t	s	l	m	v
u	p	i	r	a	t	e	s	i	p	r	l	n	l	o	o	j	e	m	e	i	c
s	i	j	w	t	s	i	n	n	s	a	c	o	r	p	a	r	r	o	t	r	m
l	r	d	s	a	e	y	f	c	g	b	g	r	u	o	m	e	i	l	o	t	p
c	h	j	o	l	l	y	r	o	g	e	r	r	r	i	s	v	u	l	n	v	i
a	s	e	m	a	s	e	n	o	b	y	l	l	i	b	s	l	q	e	t	r	v
i	m	p	i	e	c	e	s	o	f	e	i	g	h	t	s	i	s	t	c	t	s
h	n	i	l	a	c	v	m	t	f	s	c	o	i	p	m	s	n	t	d	a	t
i	n	o	v	d	d	l	a	e	e	y	n	u	a	g	d	n	n	d	e	i	o
i	n	h	t	m	s	h	e	e	p	v	v	j	n	i	m	h	c	x	z	o	c
b	u	c	c	a	n	e	e	r	t	i	e	b	t	u	i	o	b	v	c	o	k
a	s	r	g	n	i	o	l	m	n	y	g	n	p	g	h	j	u	k	w	f	a
f	v	h	m	s	o	g	b	y	b	u	m	n	s	a	t	g	y	u	j	k	d
g	f	s	a	c	m	u	r	f	o	e	l	t	t	o	b	n	h	j	h	m	e
h	t	j	k	h	s	a	e	e	r	t	u	i	o	m	n	o	j	f	r	e	e
y	j	d	a	e	q	v	z	m	k	i	i	e	a	k	l	l	m	a	s	f	g
z	b	c	s	s	d	o	c	t	o	r	l	i	v	e	s	e	y	l	q	b	m
i	r	t	p	t	e	r	t	n	e	m	n	e	e	t	f	i	f	p	x	n	j

1. Jim Hawkins

2. The location of Treasure Island was left out because the Captain, Squire, and Doctor told him to omit it.

3. Billy Bones gasped with fright.

4. They wanted the treasure map but Jim got it.

5. They outfitted a ship and sailed in search of the treasure.

6. The treasure map

7. Long John Silver

8. They had rings in their ears, whiskers curled into ringlets, tarry pigtails, and swaggering walks.

9. His left leg was cut off at the hip. He carried a crutch and used a wooden pegleg. He was tall, strong, and had a face as big as a ham.

10. The captain didn't like the men or the officer.

11. The ship's name was "Hispaniola" and the first mate was Mr. Arrow.

12. His parrot was always with him.

13. Mr. Arrow fell overboard.

14. Jim was in the apple barrel.

15. Silver stabbed Tom the pirate.

16. Ben Gunn

17. The battle happened around the stockade.

18. He wanted the Captain to hand over the treasure map and work with the pirates to find the treasure.

Fishbone Graphic Organizer

Use this graphic organizer to list the main ideas of the story.

Main Idea:

Sensory Detail Chart

Treasure Island is written in an ornate, elaborate style. Using this sensory detail chart will help students clarify the actions of the characters and the settings of the story.

Subject:

Sight:

Sound:

Smell:

Touch:

Taste:

Venn Diagram

Use the Venn Diagram to **compare** and **contrast** characters and their traits or thoughts.